ARE YOU SITTING COMFORTABLY?

Thanks to the creative team:

Senior Editor: Alice Peebles

Designer: Bryony Anne Warren

and Collaborate Agency

First published in Great Britain in 2015 by
Hungry Tomato Ltd
PO Box 181
Edenbridge
Kent, TN8 9DP

A CIP catalogue record for this book is available from the British Library.

ISBN 978-1-910684-078

Printed and bound in China

Discover more at www.hungrytomato.com

BRAIN BENDERS

ARE YOU SITTING COMFORTABLY?

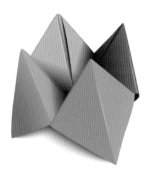

by Dr. Gareth Moore

HUNGRY TOMATO™

Contents

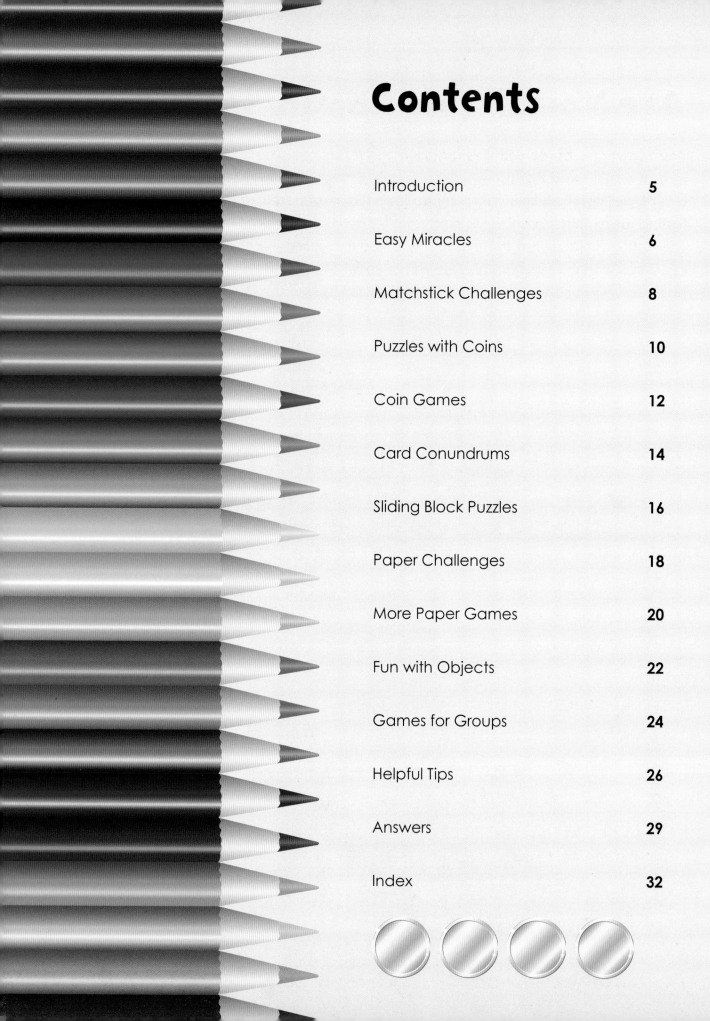

Are You Sitting Comfortably?

You'll never be bored with this fantastic collection of household challenges, and all you'll need is basic objects you can find around the home. So take a seat, get comfortable, and prepare for a range of perplexing puzzles and testing tasks! There are tips for each challenge at the back of the book, as well as solutions if you need them. And once you've solved the given challenges, see if you can come up with some of your own using the same objects. You can try them out on your friends and family! Have fun!

Dice decision

For this trick you'll need three dice, which you could borrow from a couple of board games if you don't have any handy. You'll also need a glass or some other object that you can see through from underneath.

Ask a friend to drop the three dice into a glass, then hold it up, look through the bottom and add up the numbers they can see on the dice. They shouldn't let you see the numbers or tell you the total.

Now they should pass you the glass and, without looking underneath, you can instantly tell them their total – magic!

This is a really easy trick to do. Just add up the numbers on top of the three dice, subtract this sum from 21, and that's the total they counted on the underside of the dice. So, if the total on top of the dice was 15, you would calculate 21 - 15 to make 6, which was their answer!

Why does this trick always work?

Need help with solving these puzzles? Turn to pages 26 to 28 for helpful tips.

(5)

Easy Miracles

Are you sitting comfortably? Then I'll begin to show you some amazing games and tricks that you can try out with simple, everyday objects. You don't need any special equipment, just common items that you or a friend will probably have. On these pages, for example, you need just your hands, your eyes and a piece of paper!

1 The vanishing colour

Close your right eye, and hold this book as far out in front of you as you can.

You can see all three of these coloured discs below, as you would expect.

Now look at the blue disc on the right-hand side and slowly move the book towards you, keeping your right eye shut all the time.

As the book gets closer, a funny thing happens. First, the red disc disappears!

If you look at the red disc directly it will appear again, so keep looking at the blue disc. You will see it disappear out of the corner of your eye.

Then keep moving the book closer, and all of a sudden the red disc reappears and the green disc disappears instead!

It's an amazing trick because you don't expect objects to vanish suddenly...

Can you explain why this happens?

2 Square dance

Take a square of paper, and cut it up into the four shapes shown here. Start by making the diagonal cut along the edge of the large yellow shape, then cut the top piece in two along the vertical join with the red piece. Finally, cut the top left piece in two as shown.

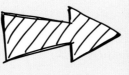

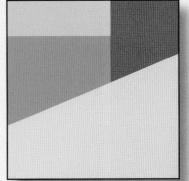

Can you explain it?

Now rearrange the four shapes like this...

Why does rearranging the shapes mean that one doesn't fit into the square any more? Try it on your friends to amaze them, too!

3 An extra finger

Can you make a ghostly third finger appear to float in front of your face, as shown here? The secret is to hold your hands in a particular position relative to your eyes. Can you work out where?

Need help with solving these puzzles? Turn to pages 26 to 28 for helpful tips.

7

Matchstick Challenges

You might have come across 'matchstick' puzzles before, where the aim is to rearrange a set of matches to solve a puzzle. You don't need to have any actual matches for these games – you can use pens or pencils, straws or even blades of grass to have a go yourself!

1 Matching squares

Start by laying out your 'matchsticks' as shown here:

This is the challenge: can you remove just **two** matches to leave only two squares and no matches that aren't part of a square? You aren't allowed to touch any of the other matches!

2 Triangle teaser

Set up six 'matchsticks' as shown here, to make one triangle and one square.

Can you move just **three** matches to create eight triangles?

You can't break any of the matches into pieces or move any matches other than the three you choose.

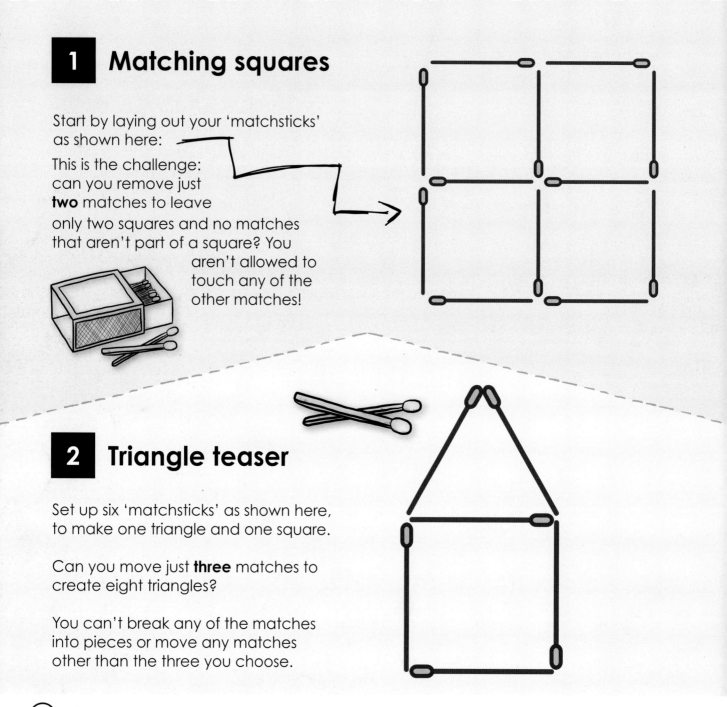

3 Something fishy

Arrange your 'matchsticks' as shown here, so that they look like a fish swimming to the left.

By moving just **three** matchsticks, can you make the fish swim to the right?

The new fish should look like the mirror image of the first fish.

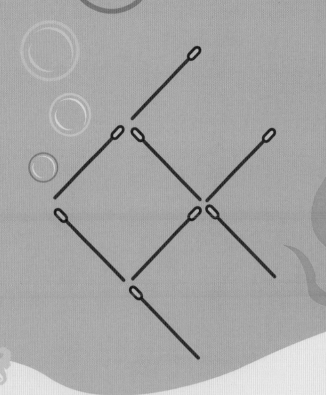

4 Stick numbers

Lay out your 'matchsticks' so that they look like the sum "4 – 3 = ", as here. Can you move **three** matches to give a valid sum, so that what's on the left of the equals sign equates to what's on the right?

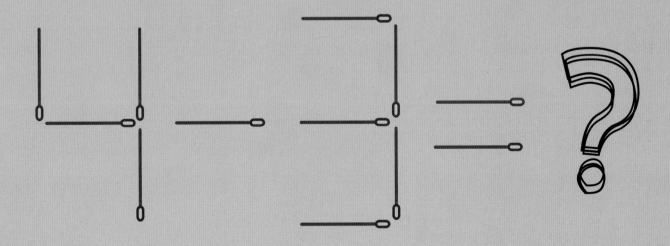

Need help with solving these puzzles? Turn to pages 26 to 28 for helpful tips.

Puzzles with Coins

To solve the puzzles on these two pages you'll need some pennies or counters – or even scraps of paper, or anything about the size of a penny that will cover one of the puzzle squares. You may find it easier to re-draw these puzzles onto a sheet of paper, so that coins can comfortably fit over the squares in each puzzle.

1 Maze of no repeats

For each of these puzzles, you place pennies, or similar items, that fits over, some numbers, so that no number can be seen more than once in any row or column. You must place them so that the squares without pennies remain connected together, like the paths on a maze. That way you can travel from one empty square to another empty square just by sliding an extra coin around the finished puzzle.

Here's an example of a solved puzzle. The 'coins' are slightly transparent so that you can see the numbers underneath. Notice how all the squares without coins are connected together in one area – that's an important part of the rules.

1	3	1
1	2	3
3	3	1

3	3	2
2	1	3
3	1	2

3	3	1
1	2	1
3	1	3

4	2	3	4
1	3	4	2
1	2	1	4
2	4	1	4

2 Submarine search

You'll need some pennies, counters or similar items to play these games, too. The aim is to find the hidden fleet of submarines, and place a coin on each square that hides a submarine. There are some shaded squares with numbers on, which are islands. The numbers give the total count of all the submarines in the row and column where the island is. Submarines can't touch either each other or an island, not even diagonally.

Take a look at this example below. Notice how the 2 at the bottom left is correct because there is a total of two ships when you count up the column and along the row that the island is in. Notice also how none of the ships touch either each other or an island, not even diagonally.

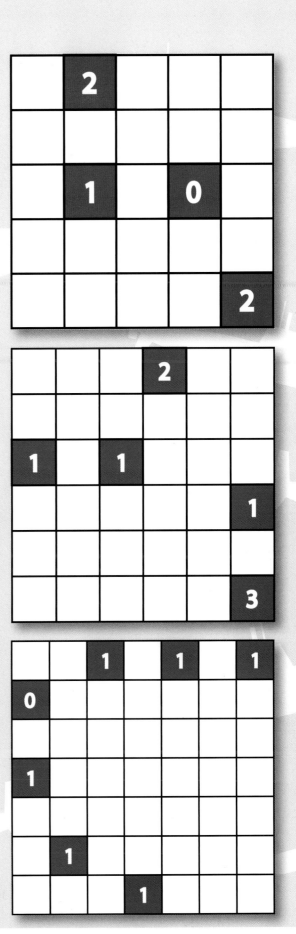

Need help with solving these puzzles? Turn to pages 26 to 28 for helpful tips.

(11)

Coin Games

There are lots of things you can do with coins besides spend them! Magicians sometimes use them for tricks, but on these pages you'll look at other things you can do with them – without leaving your chair.

1 Moving coins

You'll need six coins for this puzzle. Start by arranging them on the table so that they look like the coins on the left:

Can you rearrange them in just three moves into a hexagon, so that they look like the picture on the right?

It sounds easy, but you can only slide coins along the table rather than pick them up, which means that if a coin is blocked by another one, then you can't move it.

There's also an extra rule: whenever you finish sliding a coin, you always have to leave it so that it is touching exactly two other coins. Good luck!

2 Touching coins

Here's another coin game that involves how many times coins touch each other. This one sounds as though it should be easier, but you might find it quite tricky! Set out four coins like this:

Now, can you work out how to rearrange those coins so that every coin is touching all three other coins?

3   Tossing a coin

Have you ever tossed a coin to choose heads or tails? Professional sports players sometimes do this before a game to decide who begins play – in a tennis match, for example.

The sides of a coin are large in comparison to its edge, so when you throw it up in the air, you can be pretty certain it will land on one of its sides, rather than its narrow edge! You probably can't even balance a coin on its edge, unless it's really thick.

In practice, it's so extremely unlikely that a coin will ever land on its edge that we can consider the 'probability' of this to be zero. A probability is a number from zero to one which tells you how likely something is to happen. Zero probability means it will never happen, and a probability of one means that it is certain to happen. For example, the probability of the sun rising tomorrow morning is one. If a probability is between zero and one, it just tells you how often, on average, that event will happen – so a probability of a half means that something will happen half the time. Easy!

Try tossing a coin 30 times. Each time it lands, write down whether it landed on heads or tails. Then add up the number of heads and the number of tails. You will have approximately 15 heads and 15 tails, because both heads and tails are equally likely. In other words, the probability of getting heads on any coin toss is a half, as is the probability of getting tails. It doesn't matter what the previous result was – on each throw the probability of heads or of tails is always a half. If you're not convinced of this, try another 50 tosses!

Try this challenge. If you toss two coins at the same time, what is the probability that both will land on heads or both on tails? Try and work out what you expect the result to be first, by thinking about the various possibilities. Then try it out 40 times with the coins, keeping a count of how many times you get both heads or both tails. How often does this happen? Is it about a quarter, or about a third, or about half of the time? Does this match what you expected?

Need help with solving these puzzles? Turn to pages 26 to 28 for helpful tips.

Card Conundrums

You'll need a pack of playing cards to try the games on this page. If you can't find a pack of normal playing cards, then special cards from any other game that uses cards will do.

1 The magic card

First, count out 27 cards and put the rest of the deck away. Make sure all the cards are different or this trick won't work!

Deal a row of three cards, face up, from left to right. Keep dealing more rows of three cards until you have three columns of cards, each made up of nine rows.

Each row of cards should overlap the previous row a bit, so that you can pick a column up without changing the order of the cards.

Next, ask a friend to choose a card but only tell you which column it is in. Slide each column into its own pile, and reassemble the piles so that the pile including your friend's card goes in the middle. Once you have all the cards back in a single pile, turn it over so that they are face down in your hands.

Now repeat the whole process, dealing from the top of the deck and turning the cards over as you go so that they are face up again. Again ask your friend to pick a pile, and again pick up the three piles in such a way that your friend's pile goes in the middle. Try not to make it obvious that you are doing this!

Finally, repeat everything for a third time: deal all the cards, ask for the column, and reassemble the cards into a face-down pile with your friend's in the middle of the stack. Now here's the magic bit. Their card is guaranteed to be the 14th card in the pack, counting down from the top. But don't tell them this – let them think you're a magician! Deal the cards out and keep a secret count in your head. Once you get to the 14th card you can stop and ask them if it's their card. Amazingly, it will be!

2   Card placement

Here's a card puzzle you can try using a pencil and paper – you don't need actual playing cards.

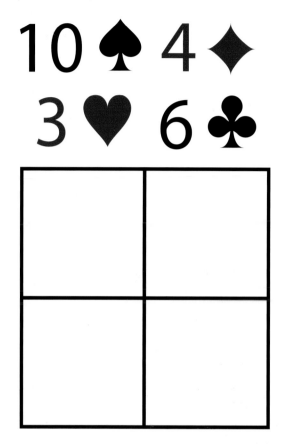

Can you work out how to place the four listed playing cards into a 2 x 2 grid, as shown in the picture, so that the following statements are all true:

- The red cards are both in the same row.
- In one of the columns, if you add up both card values then the result is equal to the value of a single card in the other column.
- In both columns, a lower value card is at the bottom.
- In the top row, the card on the left is lower in value than the card on the right.

Can you re-draw the box with the correct cards in it?

3   Card memory

Ideally, you'll have a deck of regular playing cards for this game. Remove all the black cards, so you only have the red ones left. You will now have two of each value: two Aces, two 2s and so on. If you don't have regular playing cards, you'll need a deck with some pairs of cards that you consider equal in some way. Shuffle the cards and deal them face down in two rows, each of 13 cards.

Turn over any two cards. If they are of the same value, remove them and put them aside. If they don't match in value, turn them back over so that you can't see their values. Keep doing this – turning over two cards and removing them if they match, and turning them back over if they don't. How many attempts does it take to remove them all?

This game is a great memory test, so it's well worth practising it and playing more than once. You can also play with a friend and take it in turns to turn over cards and see who can remove the most pairs!

Need help with solving these puzzles? Turn to pages 26 to 28 for helpful tips.

Sliding Block Puzzles

You might have played sliding block puzzles before, but have you ever made your own? All you need is a piece of cardboard and this book!

Take a piece of cardboard and copy out these coloured shapes as accurately as you can. Try to make them the exact same size as on this page. You might find this easier if you use a ruler. There's no need to colour the shapes if you don't want to, but you might find it helpful.

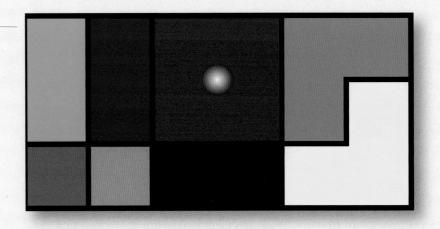

Cut out the eight shapes along the thick black lines. Now you're ready for the challenges! There are three in order of increasing difficulty, and you won't need all the pieces until the last challenge.

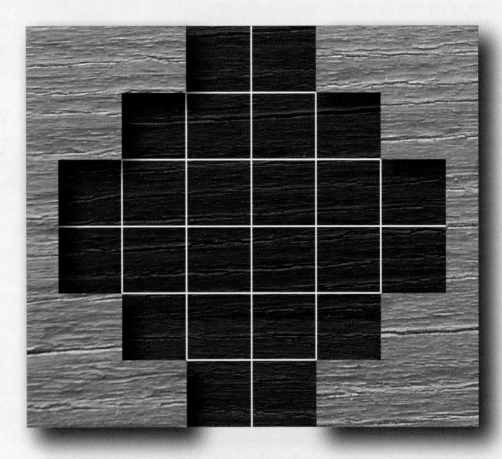

1   Sliding around

Start by arranging your pieces exactly like this on the empty wooden board. The large red square, marked with the brown dot, is at the top of the puzzle. By sliding the pieces around, can you move the red square to the bottom of the puzzle so that it will escape through the gap? Pieces can only be moved into areas on the dark, sunken part of the puzzle – they can't move onto the light outer wood. You can only move a piece by sliding it horizontally or vertically, but never diagonally. Pieces must stay aligned with the white grid lines, so each one must always end up touching another piece, a white grid line or the edge of the play area, and they must not overlap in any way.

2   Sliding further

Now have a go at this trickier challenge:

3   The ultimate challenge

If you managed to crack the first two puzzles, see if you can solve this monster puzzle. It will take a lot of moves to get the red square to the bottom!

You can also try making up your own puzzles. You could even design your own shapes for the pieces.

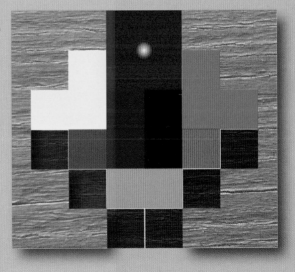

Need help with solving these puzzles? Turn to pages 26 to 28 for helpful tips.

Paper Challenges

There are lots of things you can do with paper besides write on it! For the activities on these pages you'll need plenty of paper to cut up, plus a pair of scissors.

1 Through the page

Can you walk through a hole in a piece of paper? Probably not, unless the piece of paper is incredibly large and you cut a really big hole! But there is a secret method that lets you walk through a normal-sized piece of paper, such as a page from an exercise book.

Fold the piece of paper in half, as in the first diagram below. Then make alternating cuts in the paper as shown by the bold red lines in the second diagram. The more cuts you can fit in, the better, but make sure you don't cut all the way across to make two separate pieces of paper!

Finally, cut along the fold, being careful not to cut the very first or last strip of paper. Now unfold the paper – and step right through it!

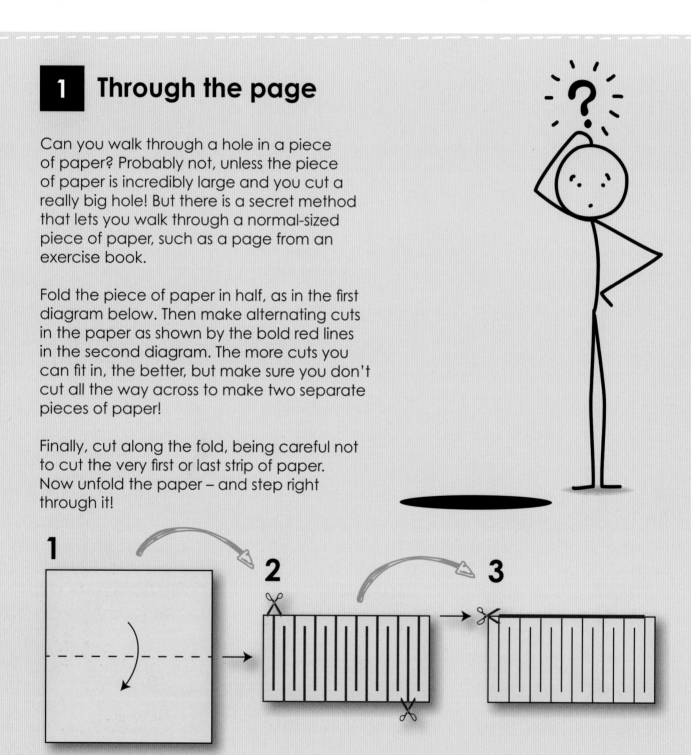

2 | A single cut

You'll need a square of paper for this activity. If need be, cut a rectangular piece to make it square. Did you know you can cut interesting shapes in a piece of paper even with a **single** straight cut through it? The secret is in how you fold it first.

1

Try this out by folding a square of paper diagonally in half, then diagonally in half again, as shown in the first two diagrams below. Finally, make one single cut across the point of the resulting triangle, as shown in the third diagram.

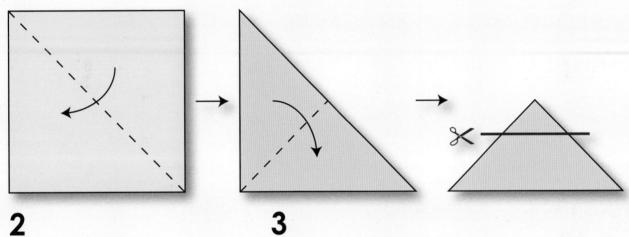

2

Now unfold the paper. You'll have a square in the middle, like this:

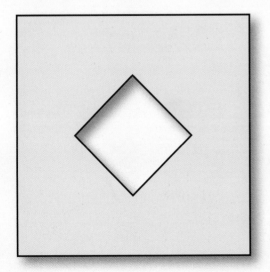

3

Using this simple technique, you can make all kinds of interesting shapes and patterns. Now here's the challenge: can you work out how to get the following results, just by folding a square of paper and again making **only one** cut?

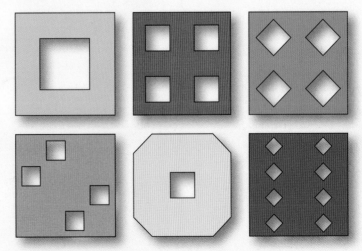

Need help with solving these puzzles? Turn to pages 26 to 28 for helpful tips.

More Paper Games

On these pages you'll use paper to tell the future and create a shape-making puzzle, plus you'll also investigate the folding properties of paper.

1 Future folding

Have you ever made a paper fortune-teller? They're easy to make and fun to play with – although they can't really tell you anything about the future!

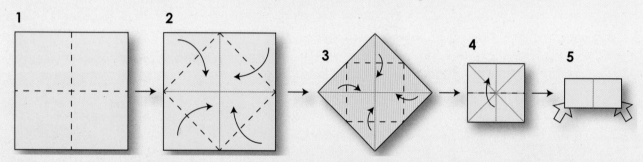

Crease a square of paper in half both ways, as shown. Fold the four corners into the centre, and the resulting set of corners into the centre, too. Finally, fold the result in half, as shown, and insert your fingers and thumbs into the four pockets you've created underneath. Now spread your fingers apart to complete your fortune-teller.

There are four petals folded into the hole on the top of the fortune-teller. Unfold one petal and on the underneath write 'Yes'. Fold the petal back in. Repeat with the other three petals, writing 'No', 'Maybe' and 'Ask again' each time.

Now you can answer any question! Get a friend to ask a question about the future and give you a number between 10 and 20. Insert your fingers into the four pockets underneath the fortune-teller, and open and close it in an alternating direction on each count. Then ask your friend to pick one of the two petals that are visible at the end of the count, and that's the answer to their question!

2 Pattern placement

Copy the following arrangement of shapes onto a piece of cardboard. You will find it easier to do this if you start by drawing the outside of the square and then draw the internal dividing lines afterwards. Finally, cut out the whole square, then the eight marked pieces.

Now, simply by placing your pieces next to each other, can you work out how to create each of these pictures shown in silhouette? The pieces shouldn't overlap at all.

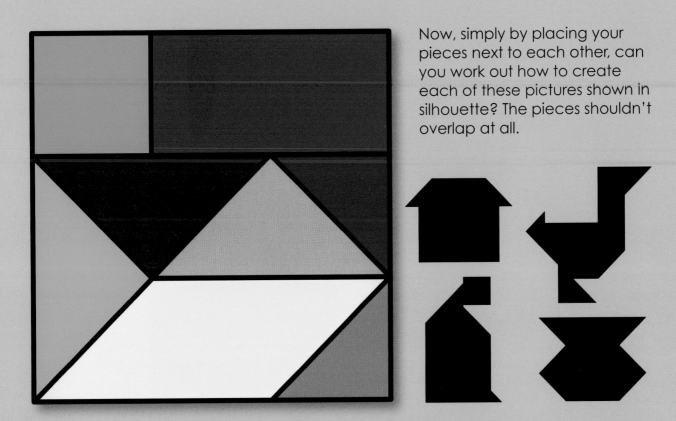

3 Folding issue

How many times can you fold a piece of paper in half, without unfolding it in between? Have a guess before you try it out, then see how close you were! Does it matter what size the piece is? If you have a piece of paper that's twice as large, can you make twice as many folds? Can some kinds of paper be folded more than others?

Need help with solving these puzzles? Turn to pages 26 to 28 for helpful tips.

21

Fun with Objects

To try out the activities on these pages you'll need a range of objects from around the house!

1 Pre-sliced banana

Have you ever peeled and sliced a banana, or had someone slice a banana for you? Wouldn't it be amazing if you could peel a banana and find that it was already sliced! It would certainly be an incredible trick.

Here's how to do it. You need a needle and thread as well as a banana, so you should definitely ask an adult for help with this.

The needle should be at least as long as the banana is thick, and you should ask your helper to thread the needle with about 30cm (1ft) of thread. It's easier if they tie it on for the purposes of this trick. Now you need to sew a square shape around the inside of the banana, just under the surface of the skin.

Try to sew as large a square as you can, which will make the banana slice better. To do this, push the needle through one side of the banana and out the other side, making sure you leave thread hanging out of the banana on both sides.

Then push the needle back into the banana at the exact point where it just came out, and sew the second side of the square – again, don't pull the end of the thread out of the banana yet. Repeat again on a third and a fourth side, until your needle comes back out of the hole where you first started. Now grip hold of both loose ends of the thread that are sticking out of the banana, and pull them tight. This will slice the banana inside its skin. You can then pull all the thread out of the banana.

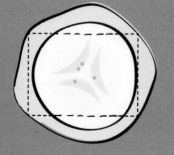

Repeat these steps until you've made as many slices in the banana as you want. Then you simply give the banana to someone who doesn't know what you've done and get them to peel it. They'll be amazed to find it already sliced!

2 Spaghetti bridge

It's easy to snap a piece of spaghetti in half, but is it always equally easy? In this activity you'll find out! You'll need a pack of spaghetti and some tape, as well as two boxes of similar height.

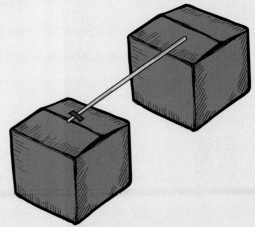

Move the boxes next to each other so that they are about 15cm (6 inches) apart. Now place one strand of spaghetti across the gap between the boxes, and tape each end to the box it is resting on. You've now formed a single-strand bridge between the two boxes.

Press down gently with your finger on the middle of the spaghetti, in the gap halfway between the boxes. Keep pressing down until the spaghetti bends by about 5cm (2 inches).

Amazingly, it doesn't snap, but bends and then returns to its original shape when you remove your finger. If you press too hard, you'll probably find that it comes untaped before it snaps!

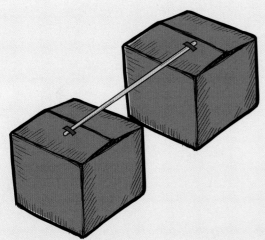

Now untape the spaghetti from one of the boxes, and move the boxes 2cm (3/4 in) closer together. Retape the spaghetti to the box and repeat the experiment. Can you still bend it just as far with one finger?

Keep moving the boxes closer together so as to shorten the spaghetti bridge until you find the point where the spaghetti finally breaks. The spaghetti breaks only when the distance between the boxes is small enough.

First, find out what this distance is. Second, can you work out why it breaks only at shorter distances?

For a further investigation, tape ten pieces of spaghetti right next to each other across the gap.

Can you still press your finger down on the spaghetti as easily as before?

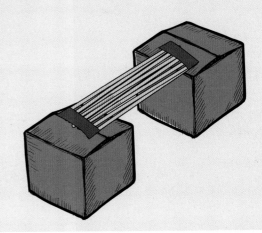

Games for Groups

You don't need to buy a fancy board game to play competitive games with friends! On these pages you'll make three of your own.

1 Target coins

You'll need coins and a piece of paper for this game, which can be played with any number of people. Start by drawing a large target on the piece of paper, made up of circles of different sizes, as in the picture below. Write a number in each circle representing the number of points it is worth, with the most points in the innermost circle. Place the paper target flat on a table top, about an arm's length from the edge of the table.

To play the game, you'll need a 10p coin. Stand next to the edge of the table and roll the coin from the very edge of the table towards the target. When it stops, if it overlaps any of the target rings, score the number of points shown on the innermost ring it overlaps. Take it in turns to roll the coin. Decide in advance what the target score is, such as 25, and the first person to reach the target score is the winner. You can make the game more complex by drawing multiple targets on different pieces of paper, perhaps with different scores on them.

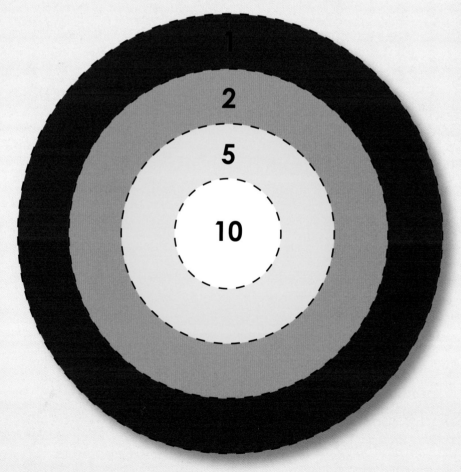

2 Pick up pencils

You'll need lots of pencils for this game, and they should be regular ones made of wood rather than fancy ones with a clip on one end. The more pencils you have, the better! You can also play with as many people as you like. Start by dropping all the pencils on the floor in a random heap. Don't drop them from too high up or the leads might break. If any land on their own, with no other pencil above or beneath them, move them onto the heap. You're now ready to start. Take turns to remove a pencil from the pile. If a player removes a pencil from the pile without any other pencil moving as a result, they keep that pencil, otherwise they must place it in a general discard pile. Keep going until there are no pencils left. The player with the most pencils at the end is the winner.

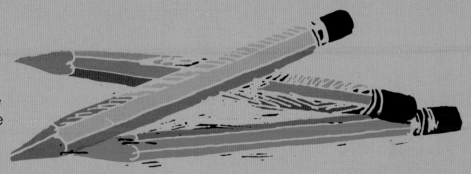

3 Last one loses

This game for two players is also played with pencils. You can equally use pens, straws or sticks if you wish. Start by laying out the pencils next to each other in a row. Now, take it in turns to remove one, two or three pencils as you choose. The winner is the player who has the last go, and removes the last pencil. Despite the simple rules, this game can be surprisingly fun to play as you try and outwit the other player! You can make the game more complicated by dividing the pencils into separate groups before you start. You then play in exactly the same way, except that you can only remove pencils from a single group at each go. The player to remove the last pencil from the last remaining group is the winner.

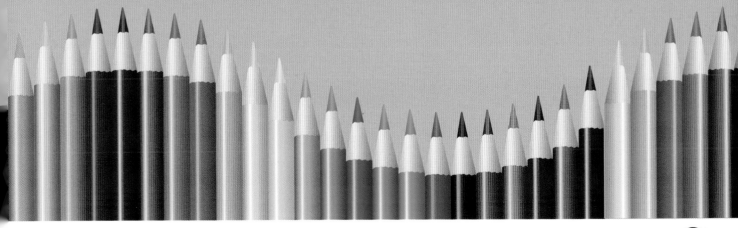

Helpful Tips

Page 5

Introduction

Examine a die. What do you notice about the numbers on opposite sides?

Pages 6 – 7

Easy Miracles

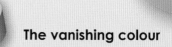

The vanishing colour

Try repeating this trick with both eyes open. Do either of the objects still vanish? What does this tell you?

Square dance

Try using a ruler to measure the dimensions of each square – perhaps not all is as it seems!

An extra finger

If you move something really close to your eyes, does it ever start to look a bit fuzzy? Does this give you a clue as to how you might create a ghostly floating finger?

Pages 8 – 9

Matchstick Challenges

Matching squares

In the opening arrangement you have four squares all the same size. But the instructions don't say that both squares in the solution have to be the same size, do they?

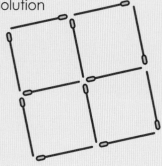

Triangle teaser

You need to make a large number of triangles here, so perhaps you need to lie some of the matches on top of each other to make lots of small triangles?

Something fishy

When you change the direction of the fish, it will also shift up or down the page a bit.

Stick numbers

You know that the solution has to show the same value on either side of the equals sign, but you can't move many matches. Can you move the equals sign instead?

Pages 10 – 11

Puzzles with Coins

A maze of no repeats

To get going on the first puzzle, consider that you have two number 1s in the middle column, which means that one of them must be covered. You can try out both options, and if you do you'll find that covering the middle square of the puzzle doesn't work so you must have to cover the other one.

There aren't many options to try. Pick one and see if it works out. If not, try another.

Submarine search

You can solve these puzzles entirely by logic, if you wish. Every time you place a coin, you eliminate lots of options because coins can't touch either along a side or diagonally. In the puzzle at the top of the page, there are only two squares where you

can place coins that will be visible from the '2' island in the first row without breaking the rules, so you can place these two coins immediately. Once you've done that, count how many coins are visible from the other islands – are you finished already?

Pages 12 – 13

Coin Games

Moving coins

To end up with the given coin arrangement, one of the two coins in the centre will have to move. You don't want it to get trapped, so move it as soon as you can.

Touching coins

Try picking up coins. This puzzle is much easier if you use actual coins or counters, rather than thinking about it with a piece of paper!

Tossing a coin

For the challenge part of this activity, think about this: what results are possible when you toss two coins at the same time? You might get heads on the first coin and tails on the second, or tails on the first and heads on the second, for example. What other options are there? Are the options all equally likely?

Page 15

Card Conundrums

Card placement

You know that both red cards are in the same row, so the 3 and 4 go on the same row. You also know that the lower value card is at the bottom, which therefore means that the 3 and 4 go on the bottom row and the 6 and 10 go on the top row. Once you've worked this much out, the rest should be a little easier.

Pages 16 – 17

Sliding Block Puzzles

You might need a little patience to solve these. If you get really confused, you can always move the pieces back to the opening arrangement and try again. If you can remember the positions you've already tried, you won't keep going round in circles!

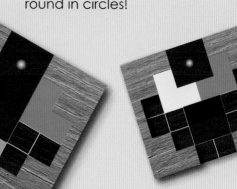

Page 19

Paper Challenges

A single cut

In the example you folded the paper diagonally in half and then cut the point off. To make all the other shapes, you only ever need to fold the paper horizontally, vertically or diagonally in half – although you may have to fold it two or more times – then make a cut. Unfold it to see the result.

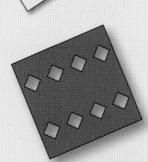

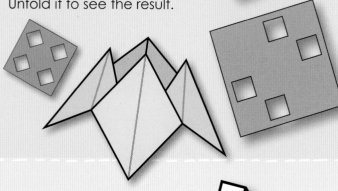

Page 21

More Paper Games

Pattern placement

You only coloured one side of the card to remind you that you can't turn over any pieces, which means you only have one option for the yellow parallelogram. Try and work out how different parts of each picture were made, but if you get stuck just move on and try a different picture.

You can also make up your own pictures by arranging the pieces as you please – or you can arrange them randomly and then decide what they look like!

Folding issue

You can vary the size of the paper – and you can also vary some other factor. What else varies between different types of paper, other than what's written or printed on them?

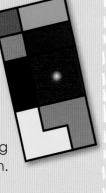

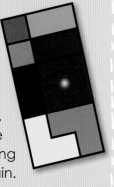

Answers

Page 5   Introduction

The opposite sides  of a die always add up to 7. Look at a real die to convince yourself! This means that if you take the value on one side of a die and subtract it from 7, you find out the value on the other side. The trick hides this fact by using three dice, whose three sets of opposite sides must then sum to 7 + 7 + 7 = 21. By subtracting the total of the top values from 21, we find out the total of the hidden values on the opposite sides.

An extra finger

Hold your two fingers apart, as in the left and right of the picture, and move them towards your eyes, so they are only 3 cm (1in) away. Between your eyes, just above your nose, you'll see a ghostly, floating 'third finger'! This is because your fingers are so close to your eyes that what you see with your left and right eyes is very different, and your brain finds it difficult to make sense of it.

Pages 6 – 7   Easy Miracles

The vanishing colour

The shapes vanish because each of your eyes has a blind spot where it can't see anything. Normally you aren't aware of this because everything in front of you can be seen by at least one of your eyes, so your brain can fill in the entire scene. This is why you need to close one eye for this to work. The blind spot is a region towards the centre of each eye that has so many connections with your brain that there's no space for the part that looks out at the world. So, if the object you're looking at can only be seen by this part of your eye, it simply vanishes! Moving the book simply changes what is visible to your eye.

Square dance

The secret is that when the original square is reassembled into a square with a piece sticking out, the new square is not the same size as before. Measure the height of the original square and of the new square. You'll see that it's shorter! This reveals how the sticking-out piece has come about: because of the space missing from the top of the square. This area is highlighted here:

Matchstick Challenges

Matching squares

The two squares are of different sizes, and they overlap each other:

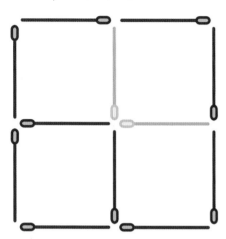

Triangle teaser

There are two sizes of triangle, and they again overlap each other:

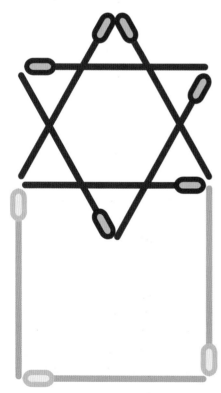

Maze of no repeats

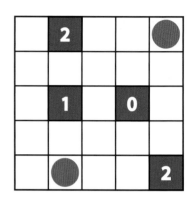

Submarine search

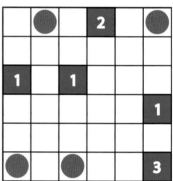

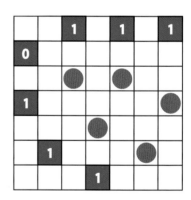

Something fishy

Stick numbers

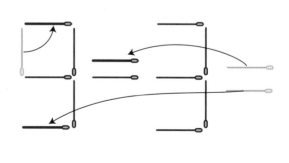

Pages 12 – 13

Coin Games

Moving coins

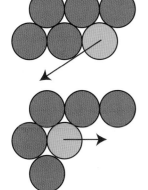

Folding issue

You probably found that you could fold a piece of paper in half no more than seven, or maybe eight, times. Beyond a certain size, it doesn't matter how large the original piece of paper is, because the problem is simply that the thickness of the paper increases to the point where it is very hard to fold. You can therefore fold really thin paper, such as tissue paper, probably one more time than regular paper.

Touching coins

The secret to this trick is to think in three dimensions! The only way to solve this is to arrange them like in this picture:

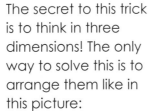

Page 15

Card conundrums

6 ♣	10 ♠
4 ♦	3 ♥

Page 21

More paper games

Pattern placement

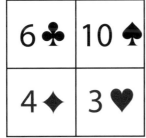

Tossing a coin

The probability of getting heads when you toss a coin is exactly half, as it is for tails. When you toss two coins together, the chance of them both being the same is also a half. You can work this out without testing it by thinking of the options, writing H for heads and T for tails:

H + H or H + T or T + T or T + H
There are four options, each equally likely as we have just worked out. Two of the four options have matching heads or tails, so we know that two in four times we'll get this result. The probability is therefore a half, since we now know that this will happen, on average, half the time. Your experimental observations will back this up!

Page 23

Fun with objects

Spaghetti bridge

The longer the span of the bridge, the more you can bend the spaghetti before it snaps. Force

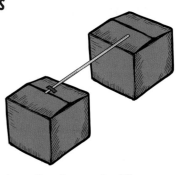

applied to a longer length of spaghetti gets spread out, so the resulting force on any given point – where it might snap – is less. As you shorten the available length of spaghetti, the force on any given point increases and it becomes more likely to snap. Using ten pieces of spaghetti spreads the force from your finger over those ten strands, meaning that the effective force on each piece of spaghetti is roughly a tenth as strong. This means that you'll need to apply a lot more force to bend all the spaghetti as much as the single piece.

Index

About the Author

Dr Gareth Moore is the author of a wide range of puzzle and brain-training books for both children and adults, including The Kids' Book of Puzzles, The Mammoth Book of Brain Games and The Rough Guide Book of Brain Training. He is also the founder of daily brain training site **www.BrainedUp.com**. He gained his Ph.D from Cambridge University (UK) in the field of computer speech recognition, teaching machines to understand spoken words.